LOOK AND FIND

Disney's

POCAHONTAS

Illustrated by Jaime Diaz Studios

Written by Virginia Tull

Illustration scripts developed by Virginia Tull
Front cover illustrated by Keith Batcheller
Lettered by Kelly Hume

Published by
Louis Weber, C.E.O.
Publications International, Ltd
7373 North Cicero Avenue
Lincolnwood, Illinois 60646

© The Walt Disney Company

Manufactured in U.S.A.

8 7 6 5 4 3 2 1

ISBN 0-7853-1188-2

PUBLICATIONS INTERNATIONAL, LTD.

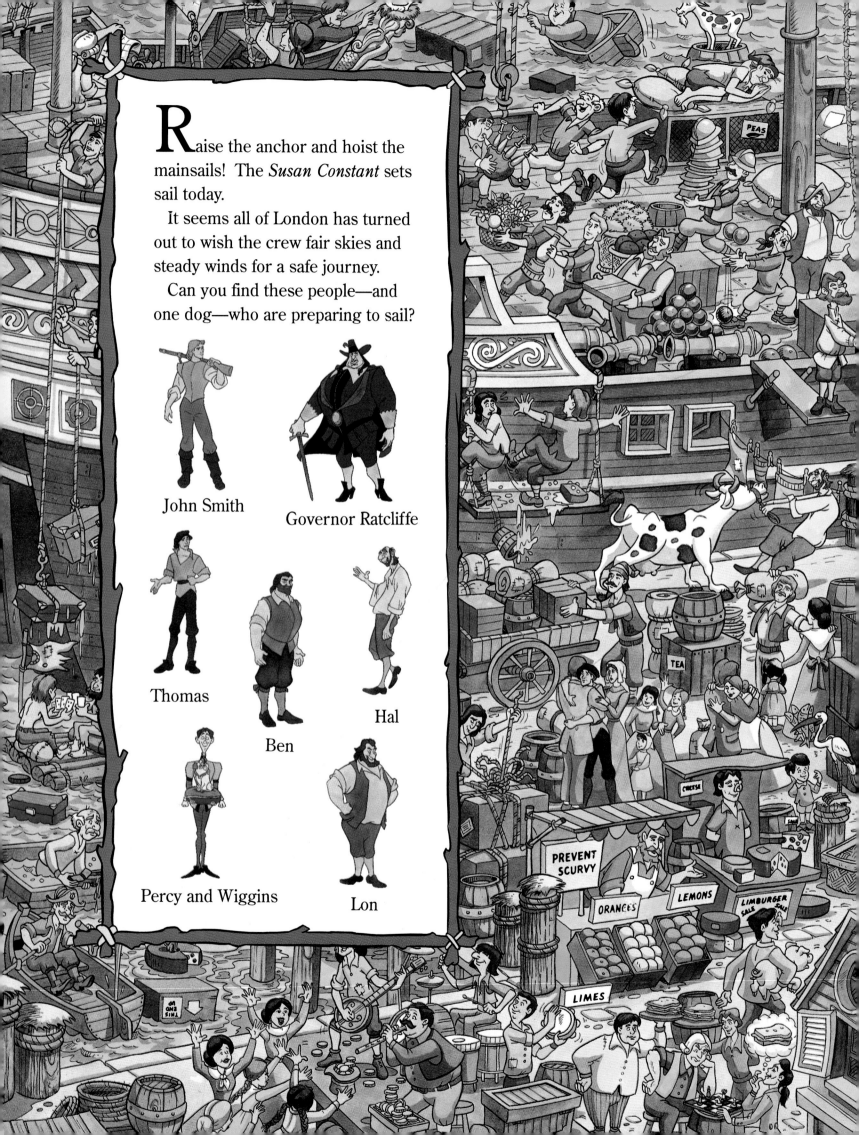

Raise the anchor and hoist the mainsails! The *Susan Constant* sets sail today.

It seems all of London has turned out to wish the crew fair skies and steady winds for a safe journey.

Can you find these people—and one dog—who are preparing to sail?

John Smith

Governor Ratcliffe

Thomas

Ben

Hal

Percy and Wiggins

Lon

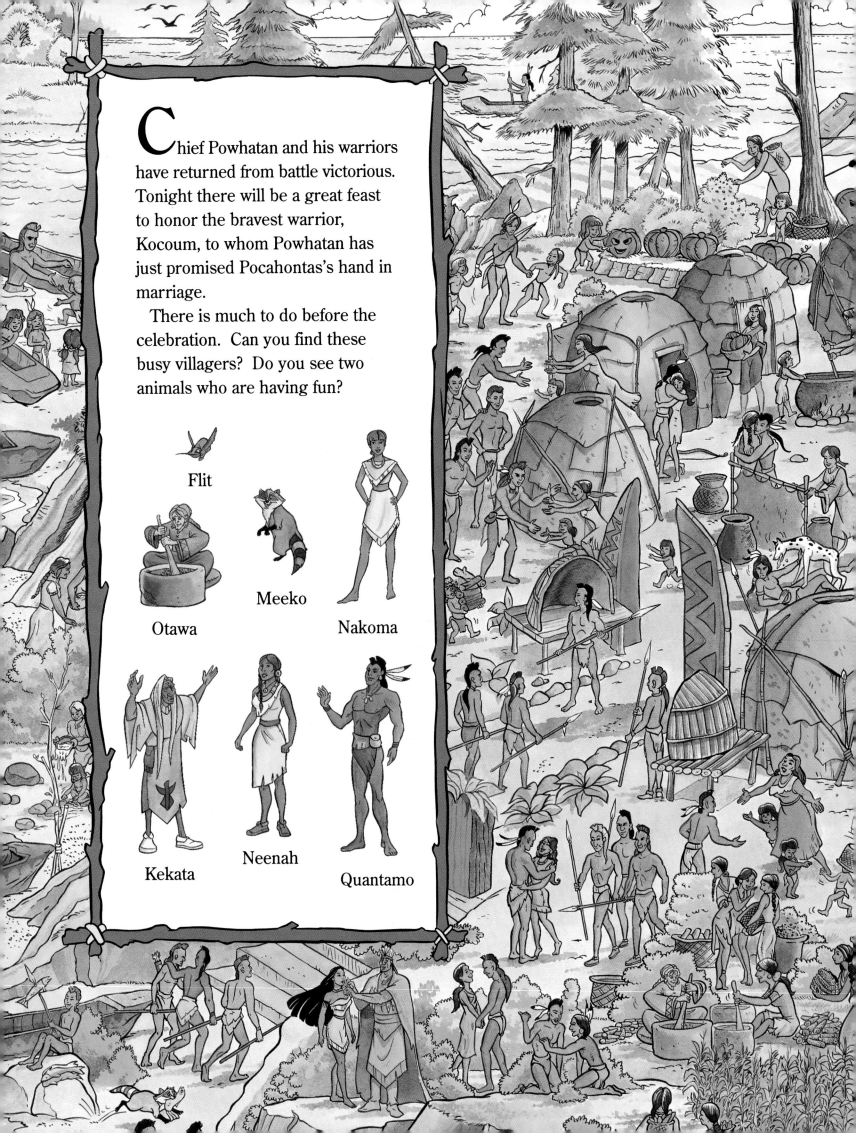

Chief Powhatan and his warriors have returned from battle victorious. Tonight there will be a great feast to honor the bravest warrior, Kocoum, to whom Powhatan has just promised Pocahontas's hand in marriage.

There is much to do before the celebration. Can you find these busy villagers? Do you see two animals who are having fun?

Flit

Meeko

Otawa

Nakoma

Kekata

Neenah

Quantamo

What is waiting just around the river bend for Pocahontas? Should she listen to her father and marry Kocoum? Or should she listen to her heart and try to follow a different path?

Find these animals that make their homes along Pocahontas's beloved river.

Boar

Bear

Skunk

Deer

Heron

Fox

Rabbit

Otter

Grandmother Willow is a wise, ancient spirit. She knows things are not always what they seem.

Except for Pocahontas and her animal friends, the enchanted glade seems empty. Look again. Can you find these objects that are not part of nature?

An arrow

A goblet

An anchor

A compass

A sword

A canoe

An hourglass

A peace pipe

Governor Ratcliffe has ordered his men to dig up Virginia until they find gold. It must be here, he thinks. Why else would the Indians want to drive the settlers away?

Can you find the gold in Virginia?

Goldenrod

Golden delicious apple

Ear of gold

Gold tooth

Golden locket

Goldfinch

Gold leaf

Pocahontas tells John Smith that if he will walk the footsteps of another, he will learn things he never knew.

Watch as the swirling wind shows how everything is connected, that life is a circle that never ends. Look for these things carried by the wind.

Can you find these footprints, too?

So many things here are new and different to John Smith. He loves taking walks with Pocahontas so she can tell him the names of the plants in this beautiful forest.

Find these interesting plants that grow where Pocahontas lives.

Hickory

Milkweed

Wild strawberry

Sassafras

May apple

Poison ivy

Persimmon

Jack-in-the-pulpit

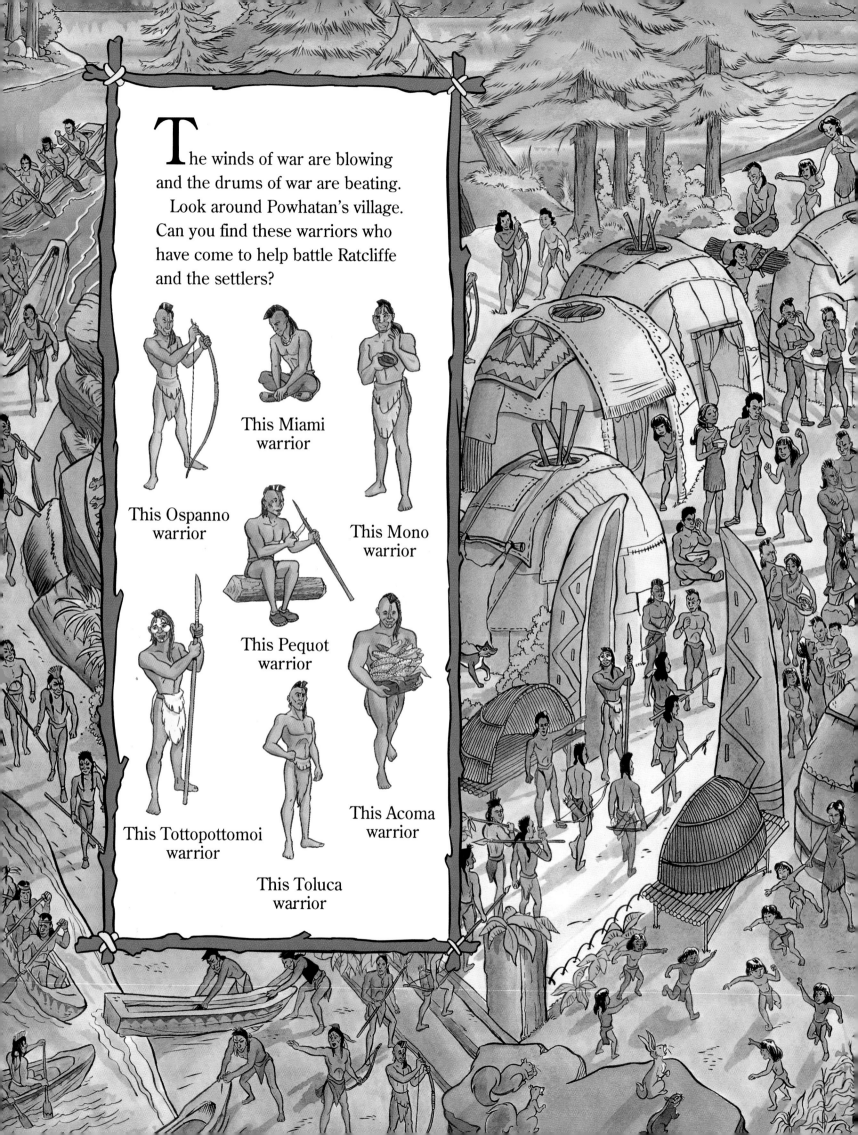

The winds of war are blowing and the drums of war are beating. Look around Powhatan's village. Can you find these warriors who have come to help battle Ratcliffe and the settlers?

This Ospanno warrior

This Miami warrior

This Mono warrior

This Pequot warrior

This Tottopottomoi warrior

This Acoma warrior

This Toluca warrior

The Powhatan people have come with Pocahontas to say good–bye to John Smith and the settlers who are taking him back to England.

The other settlers and the Powhatans are exchanging gifts that show they are willing to live together peacefully. Look for these gifts of goodwill.

This painting

This necklace

This watch

This spear

This headdress

This horn

This helmet

Go back to the Port of London where the *Susan Constant* is preparing to sail. Look for sailors doing these things.

☐ Mending a sail
☐ Tying a knot
☐ Kissing a baby
☐ Carrying a pig
☐ Swabbing a deck
☐ Playing cards
☐ Chasing a chicken
☐ Taking a nap

Go back to Powhatan's village to find helpful children doing these chores.

☐ Shucking corn
☐ Stirring stew
☐ Scraping a hide
☐ Sharpening arrows
☐ Rocking a baby
☐ Carrying firewood
☐ Planting a tree
☐ Picking berries

While paddling along the river, Pocahontas sees these baby animals. Do you see them, too?

☐ A fox pup chasing a butterfly
☐ A raccoon kit washing its hands
☐ A sleeping owlet
☐ Twin bear cubs eating berries
☐ A fawn napping near its mother

Go back to Grandmother Willow's enchanted glade to see if you can find more hidden objects.

☐ A violin
☐ A snake
☐ A spoon
☐ A watch
☐ A cup and saucer
☐ A bow
☐ A fork
☐ An ear of corn